ORIGIN

OF

PRIMITIVE MAN

(1912)

Albert Churchward

The Origin and Evolution of Primitive Man
By: Albert Churchward

Printed: December, 2003

Published and Distributed by:
LUSHENA BOOKS, INC.
607 Country Club Drive, Unit E
Bensenville, IL 60106

ISBN: 1-930097-70-0

Printed in the United States of America

The Origin and Evolution of Primitive Man

Lecture given at the Royal Societies Club
St James's Street, February 1912

BY

ALBERT CHURCHWARD

M.D., M.R.C.P., F.G.S., ETC.

AUTHOR OF "ORIGIN AND ANTIQUITY OF FREEMASONRY"
AND "SIGNS AND SYMBOLS OF PRIMORDIAL MAN"

LONDON

GEORGE ALLEN & COMPANY, LTD.

RUSKIN HOUSE, 44 AND 45 RATHBONE PLACE

1912

INTRODUCTION

So many of my friends have requested a copy of the lecture I delivered recently at the Royal Societies Club, on the "Origin and Evolution of Primitive Man," that I have decided to publish it.

The slight additions made will render it more complete and (I trust) more interesting to my readers.

The matter is practically all original, and has not, hitherto, been brought to the notice of the Public ; but the evidence in favour of my contentions is critically correct.

I am greatly indebted to my friend, Mr Trevor Haddon, R.B.A., for the skill, kindness and patience he has displayed over the drawings of the types of men which he has reconstructed from my directions.

The subject of the lecture now published constitutes a chapter in " The Origin and Evolution of the Human Race "—the book I am now compiling but cannot hope to complete before another two years.

ALBERT CHURCHWARD.

THE ROYAL SOCIETIES CLUB,
63 ST JAMES'S STREET,
LONDON, S.W.

1912.

CONTENTS

	PAGE
DIVISIONS OF PRIMITIVE MAN	13
PYGMIES' ANATOMICAL FEATURES	18
PYGMIES' PHYSIOLOGICAL FEATURES	19
PYGMIES' SPIRITUAL BELIEFS	22
MAJOR POWELL-COTTON'S OBSERVATIONS	23
DR FRAZIER'S OPINION	26
MAGIC AND ITS DEFINITION	27
EGYPTIAN OPINION	28
PYGMY DANCES	29
SPIRIT WORSHIP	31
DAWN OF RELIGION	32
BUSHMEN	36
MASABA NEGRO	37
NILOTIC NEGRO	37
PROFESSOR KEITH'S OPINION	40
PROFESSOR SOLLAS' OPINION	41
HAECKEL'S THEORY	45
ANCIENT IMPLEMENTS	49
BURIAL CUSTOMS	53
AGE OF MAN	57
LANGUAGE	58
PYGMY WORDS	59
DR A. C. HADDON'S OBSERVATIONS	60

7

LIST OF ILLUSTRATIONS

1. Paleolithic Pygmy Implements
2. Paleolithic Pygmy Implements
3. Paleolithic Pygmy Implements
4. Paleolithic Nilotic Negro Instruments
5. Paleolithic Nilotic Negro Instruments
6. Paleolithic Nilotic Negro Instruments
7. Paleolithic Nilotic Negro Instruments, Methods of Hafting
8. Paleolithic Implements
9. Implements of the Stellar Mythos People
10. Neolithic Implement, Flint Dagger
11. Prehistoric Tombs, Stellar Mythos Man
12. Prehistoric Tombs found at Uxmal, Yucatan
13. Prehistoric Tombs found at Harlyn Bay
14. Pygmies showing Characteristic Features
15. Pygmies showing Height and General Appearance
16. Pygmies showing General Appearance
17. Tasmanian Natives
18. The God Bes
19. Bushman showing Pygmy Characteristics
20. Bushmen
21. Masaba Negro
22. Masaba Negro
23. Masaba Negro
24. Nilotic Negro Children, Nilotic Negro Woman
25. Nilotic Negroes showing Characteristic Features
26. Nilotic Negro Woman, Type of First Exodus
27. Nilotic Negro, Type of First Exodus

9

28. Nilotic Negroes showing Pygmy Characteristics
29. Nilotic Negro of Second Exodus
30. Nilotic Negro Woman, Type of Second Exodus
31. The Neanderthal Skull. The Spy Skull. The Gibraltar Skull
32. The Lower Jaw of Neanderthal Skull
33. Skeleton found at Harlyn Bay
34. The Cranium of Pithecanthropus Erectus
35. The Neanderthal Cranium
36. The Ipswich Cranium
37. Modern English Cranium
38. Nilotic Negro, Types of Big Heads found in Europe
39. Squatters
40. Squatters
41. A Reconstruction of Primary Man
42. A Reconstruction of Neanderthal Man
43. A Reconstruction of the Ipswich Man
44. Map of Africa showing the Home of Primary Man
45. A Genealogical Tree of Man and the Anthropoids
46. Pure Egyptian Hieroglyphics

LECTURE

Gentlemen,—

Having been invited to give a lecture on " The Origin and Evolution of Man," I accepted with pleasure, because one of the reasons for the foundation and formation of the Royal Societies Club was for the furtherance of Science and for Social reunion. As one of your original members, I thought that the Royal Societies Club should be the first place in which to proclaim publicly the result of my researches, not all of which can yet be published as it will probably take another two years to complete my book on this subject.

From studies I have made during many years I am fully convinced that the preconceived ideas of many scientists as to the origin of the human race—as regards both place and date—are erroneous, and that the human race did not originate in Asia, or any other part of the world, but in Africa.

I will bring evidence before you which I

am sure you will acknowledge as critically correct.

The proofs of my contention against all the learned men of the present day will be objective and subjective.

The poet Pope says :

" Know then thyself, presume not God to scan—
The proper study of mankind is man."

Therefore, when and where did man make his first appearance here on this earth ?

Biblical Scholars tell you—About 6000 years ago in Asia.

The Aryanist School—In Asia about 20,000 years ago.

Many others, including most Scientists—In Asia, or in some mythical land which has now disappeared.

All of them have denied Africa as the home of Man.

But, Gentlemen, *it was in Africa that the little Pygmy was first evolved from the Pithecanthropus Erectus or an Anthropoid Ape*—in the Nile Valley and around the lakes at the head of the Nile (which in this lecture I will, for the sake of brevity, style " Old Egypt ").

From here these little men spread all over the world, North, East, South and West, until not only Africa, but Europe, Asia, North and South America and Oceania were populated by them.

He was the first—the little red man of the earth.

From the Pygmy, evolution continued progressively in the following order :—

1. Bushmen. 2. Masaba Negro. 3. Nilotic Negro. 4. Masi, and 5. Mongoloids, and then the so-called Aryanists.

My contention is, that the progress and evolution of the human race can still be studied from the lowest type of the original man as he advanced up the scale ; and that these types are still extant in some parts of the world, where the primary race has been driven away into mountains and inaccessible forests by the Nilotic Negro, and these again into lands where they have been isolated by the Stellar Mythos people into groups, with little or no intercommunication with others.

I shall divide the human race into the following groups of evolution.

1st Group—The Non-Totemic or Pre-Totemic People

The Pygmy Group includes all the so-called negrillos or negretos—all Pygmies.

All these have no Totemic ceremonies.

They believe in a Great Spirit.

They propitiate Elementary Powers and departed Spirits.

And although they have dances as Sign Language, they have no Totemic ceremonies —no written language—they speak a monosyllabic language and have a Sign and Gesture Language.

Their implements are limited and primitive.

They have no folk-lore tales.

They have no magic.

They have no initiatory rites or Totemic marks.

2ND GROUP

Bushmen and Masaba Negroes have dances like the Pygmies.

They have no Totemic ceremonies or Totems, but are the connecting links between the Pygmy race and the—

3RD GROUP—TOTEMIC

Nilotic Negro.—These have Totemic ceremonies and Totems, and the second exodus of these have what Dr Haddon has termed " Hero Cult " instead of " Hero Worship," which term I shall use, as it is, in my opinion, more expressive.

4TH GROUP

These were the Stellar Mythos people who existed as such for over 260,000 years. Their skill and knowledge may be gauged by the many great cities and the huge and marvellously fashioned blocks of stone, the remains of which may still be found in Africa, Central and South America and other places.

Two ages of these can also be separately identified ; the first exodus having Sut or Set for the Primary God and being buried with face to the south, and the second, the followers of Horus, being buried with face to the north. All in the thrice-bent position.

These were followed by the Lunar and Solar Mythos people, who are now giving place to the Christian.

I will therefore commence with the evidence of the Pygmy being the first man and evolved in Africa.

Firstly.—It has been stated that these little people are a degenerate race.

Secondly.—That they have no language of their own, but only words they have learnt from the surrounding tribes of negroes.

Thirdly.—That they have no belief in a future life or a Great Spirit.

All the foregoing statements are incorrect.

The Pygmies are not a degenerate race ; for this reason—you cannot degenerate Anatomically or Physiologically.

We find them as *little people*—following the well-known laws of evolution, that animals at first developed as a small species, and then grew large.   For instance, the first form of the elephant was as quite a little creature in comparison with its present size.   And in like manner the human was evolved from a little man.

The height of the Pygmy averages from 1·15 to 1·37 metres.

His weight averages from three stone to seven stone.

His Osteo anatomy is more primitive than the earliest skeletons (or parts of skeletons) that have been found in various parts of the world.   I contend that in the reconstruction of these remains it is proved that they correspond to the Nilotic Negro, and to the Stellar Mythos people.   Here let me say that, as one would expect to find after all these thousands of years of their existence, there are lower and higher types of the Pygmy, although they have been cut off from the world and from all intercommunication by being driven into forests and mountains where the Nilotic Negro did not follow.   Those Pygmies who have not intermarried with the surrounding tribes are always the same, except when climate, etc., has had some effect. But there is no "throw-back," as you sometimes find amongst the later tribes.

There are six distinct tribes well known in Africa alone.

1. The Akka. Average height of thirty-eight given by Deniker 1·378 metres ; and thirty measured by Emin Pasha average 1·36 metres.

2. The Balia.
3. The Tikki-Tikki.
4. The Batwa.
5. The Wambutta.
6. The Banzungu.

Outside Africa they still exist—in New Guinea, New Hebrides, the forest of Bolivia in South America, the mountains in China, the Philippine Islands, the Sakais in the Malay Peninsula, and in Northern India. They have been exterminated in Europe, North America, Japan, Australia and Tasmania, but I have no doubt they are to be found in other places not yet explored.

They are not negroes, but negrillos or negretos.

We will take their Anatomical features first.

B

Some of them are broad-chested, short-necked, strong-looking, muscular and well-made.

Colour.—Varies from a chocolate brown to rather reddish tint.

Their arms—Look longer in proportion to that of the European, but it is only *the forearm* ; this is at least 1 p.c. longer than that of the European—in some a little more.

The bones—Ulna and Radius are wider apart than in the European or the yellow race.

Hair.—It is important to notice this.   It is not woolly or kinky like the Negro's, but is rolled closely into little balls—discrete peppercorn.   It is the same in the male and in the female all over the body, both on the Pubes and Axilla, and is the same in length, colour and section.   The hair of those that I have seen has not been black, but rather of a peculiar very dark greenish-grey, of a lustreless appearance. *Transverse section ovoid-eleptic.*

Nose.—The root of the nose is exceptionally flattened—very broad.   The tip is broad and flattened and the alæ greatly expanded, although in some this varies to a greater extent than one could believe without seeing.

Eyebrows.—Well formed, and different from the Negro's.

Teeth. Well formed, and rather large for such little men. They crunch up bones with ease.

The Palate is elongated.

The Lips are quite characteristic. They have not the massive, fleshy, everted lips of the Negro, but rather long narrow lips. The upper has a noteworthy subnasal projection ; and when drinking or speaking the combination of the flattened nose and the lips give a striking Simian appearance.

Steatopygia.—In some there is very distinct enlargement and development of the gluteal region—as in the Bushman.

Ears are small, the *lobules not well developed; and in some the pinnia is crudely formed.*

The chin is small in all, and the mandible is narrowest and inclined to be pointed.

Brain. — Average weight in a healthy Pygmy is 900 *grammes.*

PHYSIOLOGICAL CONDITIONS

Abdomen.—In all the Pygmies and Pygmean races there is an extraordinary prominence of the abdomen, which has been attributed to over-feeding and a large liver. In this I am sure you will agree with me that, if it was so, the Pygmy might be one of the late humans in evolution instead of being one of the primary. But this prominence is caused by no such modern reasons. *It is a primal condition of man*, and proves his near affinity to the Anthropoid Ape. It is owing to the cæcum being placed high up in the lumbar region ; from it the colon is bent downwards to the right, and the iliac fossa, thus becoming largely distended, pursues a sigmoid course across the abdomen, resulting in this appearance. Now, if my contention is right, the reason for this is apparent.

In the animal, the important processes of herbivorous digestion takes place in the large intestine. In such animals a very large proportion of the food—namely, the proteins and carbohydrates—is shut up within the cellulose walls of the vegetable cells ; *and since none of the higher vertebrata have the power of producing a cellulose digesting ferment in their alimentary canal*, these food stuffs would be lost to the body were not some other means provided for the solution of the cellulose. This means is through the agency of bacteria. The mass of vegetable matter which accumulates in the cæcum is a breeding-ground for bacteria, and more especially for the bacteria which feeds upon cellulose. These bacteria dissolve into cellulose and ferment it with the production of fatty acids, methane, carbon dioxide and hydrogen ; and by this means the contents of the vegetable cells are set free, and can be absorbed by the walls of the large intestine. *Thus we see the importance of the large intestine in the lower types of " homo," who live in low conditions and depend for their nutriment on coarse vegetable foods ; whereas in civilised man this condition is not found, it not being required, for he has risen, by evolution, to that state in which he selects the most digestible food stuffs, and prepares them by grinding, cooking, etc., for the process of digestion, separating all the harder parts, so that the larger intestine has little or no work to do. Now, in the Pygmy we find that the cæcum and larger intestine are more developed than in any other human, and he possesses bacteria in this intestine which do not exist in civilised man.* Moreover, as we have advanced by evolution so this large cæcum and large intestine have become smaller, as can be seen in the following order :—Bushmen, Masaba Negro, Nilotic Negro, Masi, Yellow man, White man. Mr Arbuthnot Lane, Surgeon to Guy's Hospital, by excising the whole of the colon has proved that the white man is just as well without it as with it, and in many cases is better. *The above proves absolutely that the Pygmies are not a degenerate race, but the primary one.*

The second point is that they have *no Language.* Sir H. Johnston, as well as others, has stated that they had no language of their own, only speaking the words from surrounding tribes ; but afterwards he acknowledged in *The Lancet,* in answer to a letter of mine in that paper in 1905, that he was wrong. They have a limited monosyllabic language, also a language of signs and symbols. Mr Tovey Cozens, who lived amongst them for two years, also agrees with me that they have a language of their own, although it is quite possible that they may have learnt some words from surrounding tribes.

Age.—It is difficult to say to what age they live. When asked, the reply was " Many moons," as they reckon by Lunar time only.

The third point.—*That they have no belief in a future life or Great Spirit. This also is not correct.*

They take great care of anyone who is defective, because they say, if they do not, the Great Spirit will come and do them harm.

They build little Spirit Houses and put food there for their departed friends—a propitiation of the Spirit.

They told Mr Giel they believe that when they die their spirit enters a great serpent, and this serpent comes to see them, remains a few days, and then goes away. The serpent does not harm them nor they it.

This is their only way or mode of expressing their belief that they have a future life in the Spiritual world. It is an expression in sign language, *and not a belief in reincarnation,* as some have stated.

They propitiate elemental power.

The following statement by Major P. H. G. Powell-Cotton contains further proof of their belief in a Supreme Spirit :—

" It was during a forest storm that I received my first inkling that the Pygmies believed in a Supreme Spirit. One evening, about five, as they came to fetch me, after lying throughout the day in the forest, a wind sprang up and dried twigs and leaves came rustling down, while every now and then a dead branch or limb crashed to the ground. With quick glances to right and left at the tree-tops, my head tracker hastened his steps; then, uttering a shrill whistle, he placed his left hand to his mouth, made a sneezing sound into it and threw it above his head in an attitude of supplication. As the storm grew and the thunder came nearer, I saw him darting anxious looks on either side, till he espied a little shrub, with leaves like a willow. Gathering a bunch of these, he pressed them into the palm of his hand, sneezed over them and again extended his hand in supplication over his head. Presently a tremendous thunderclap burst overhead, whereupon he hastily plucked a larger leaf, wrapped the other up in it, and tied them to the top of a stick, which he then held aloft, and every now and then, to the accompaniment of shrill whistles, waved it round his head. On return to camp I obtained from him an explanation of these strange proceedings. The first part of his ceremonies was an appeal to the Supreme Spirit to send away the tempest, but, as the storm continued, he besought protection for us from falling branches torn off by the wind."

Here we have the Pygmy " offering propitiation to the elemental power "—the first origin of religion. The earliest mode of worship recognisable was in propitiation of the superhuman power. This power was of necessity

*elemental, a power that was objectified by means
of the living type ; and of necessity the object
of propitiation, invocation and solicitation
was the power itself, and not the types by which
it was imaged in the language of signs.* If
we use the word worship, it was the propitiation of the power in the thunder and
the storm—not the thunder or storm itself.

"Again, during our wanderings in the forest,
we came across many curious little structures
—diminutive dwellings, which we were told
were ghost-houses." *These were built to propitiate the shades of departed chiefs,* who, until
a resting-place is provided for them, nightly
disturb the Pygmy villages. *There the people
sacrifice and place food for the spirits of the
departed.* We obtained much interesting information regarding the existing of religious
beliefs, even amongst these Pygmies, and
learnt that in some spot in the innermost
recesses of the forest an imposing religious
rite takes place on certain occasions, in which
an altar is erected, whereon offerings are laid
while the Pygmies arrange themselves in a
semicircle and perform their devotions.

Dr Schmidt, in his recent book on the
Pygmy, believes that they received " a gift "
direct from the Supreme Being. I contend

that they obtained their religious ideas direct
from observation of the elemental powers.
Certainly we agree that the Great Spirit
might have, and probably did intend that
their brain cells should be capable of observation and thinking ; it would only be evolution, the natural law of creation. On this
point we agree with Dr Schmidt, but on
no other.

With the Pygmy the elements of life themselves are the objects of recognition, and the
elementary powers were (and are) propitiated.
This was the beginning which preceded the
Zootype and this they expressed in sign
language, and this preceded Mythology and
Totemism. There are no legends or folk-
lore tales connected with the Pygmy, no
mythology, for he was and is pretotemic.
He has no magic. Sign Language is far older
than any other form of sociology.

*Pygmies possess no magic, but they do possess
religious ideas. This proves that Dr Frazier's
opinion of this is as erroneous as his opinion
" that all tribes have developed all their religious
ideas, Totems and Totemic ceremonies, from
their own surroundings."*

Speaking of this evolution of thought, he
states that he believes " *those that practise*

magic represent a lower intellectual status, and that it has preceded religion."

Now magic is very late in comparison with religious ideas, probably thousands of years; and we do not meet this evolution until we come to the Nilotic Negro, and even then amongst the most primitive it is questionable if it is used by them. Not until the second exodus of these do we find it; it was first used when the elementary powers were born of the first Mother—the old Mother Earth, Ta Urt of the Egyptians, of no sex, who reproduces no children, male or female, but was a provider of food and life as represented by the seven elemental powers.

Magic is the power of influencing the elemental or ancestral spirits.

Magical words are words with which to conjure and compel. Magical processes were acted with the same intent—*i.e.* magical incantations which accompany the gesture signs. The appeal is made to some superior superhuman force—*i.e.* one of the elemental powers in mythology, which become the gods and goddesses in the later cults.

The amulets, charms, and tokens of magical power that were buried with the dead afterwards become fetish on account of what

28 ORIGIN AND EVOLUTION

they imagined symbolically, and Fetish-Symbolism is Sign Language in one of its ideographic phases.

Let us now take into consideration of our argument :

What was the opinion of the Pygmies by the old Egyptians during the time they were working out their mythologies ? and how have they left a record of their ideas and beliefs ? This is answered in unmistakable language ; *the Egyptians represented the first type of homo by the Pygmy—at the creation of the Solar Cult.*

Hitherto all through the Stellar and Lunar Cults the representation was by Zootypes.

During the Solar Cult, man was first represented, and the Pygmy was thus portrayed as the God Bes. Thus the Pygmy was recognised as primary homo.

The Pygmies represented the earliest human form of the seven primal powers—not giants ; these giants were the Zootypes of the superhuman powers—not human—but the Pygmies are.

In the Egyptian Solar Mythos, Ptah was the great Architect of the Universe, but not the universe as a cosmological creation. Ptah was a Pygmy, and with his seven assistant Pygmies, created Amenta, or the Lower

Earth, which was represented by a passage hollowed out of the earth, as an ideograph of the earth that was formed by Ptah and his seven Pygmies—formed for the passage of the " manes " and the Sun and Moon for the first time in the Solar Mythos. It was through the earth, and not around the earth as formerly in Stellar and Lunar Mythos. In the Stellar and Lunar Cults the " manes " or soul had to pass around the earth, and was carried to the Celestial North by a super-human power that was preanthropomor-phically represented by Zootype giants.

Thus we see that the old wise men of Egypt first represented the Solar in human type, and that that type was primordial man—represented by the Pygmies : the old Egyptians knowing that they originated or descended from these.

Dances—Best Dancers in the Old World

The Dance is Sign Language, and is used and performed as sacred mysteries in *various modes*, by which *the thought, the wish, the want* is expressed in act instead of (or in addition to) words which they do not possess. They were too poor in articulate words, therefore these ceremonial words were established as the means to memorise facts in Sign Language, when there were not any written records of the human past. In these dances the knowledge was *acted, the Ritual was exhibited and kept in ever-living memory by continued repetition, and the mysteries, religious or otherwise, were founded on the basis of action.* These are acted symbolically and dramatically, the more to impress them upon the minds of the individuals concerned, they having only this Sign Language to enable them to transmit from one generation to another their then ideas and beliefs as regards the departed spirits, the Spirit world and the life hereafter. How many thousands of years did man exist working out this Sign Language and formulating articulate sounds ?

When man began to observe and think, he would see different forces at work throughout nature ; he must have noticed the changes of the Moon, the movement of the Stars, the seasons of the year and the different forces of the Universe, Celestial and Terrestrial. Each of these powers, these forces in nature, would appeal to him ; and having only a limited number of words to express his thoughts, he would naturally adopt an animal, a bird, or fish, or something that he could see. The association with it would convey to his mind the idea of one of the powers or forces, which he would thus represent by a sign or drawing of the animal or bird or object—sometimes a compound one, as we see in the Egyptian later.

Thus, as we see, they represent death and darkness by a crocodile's tail, because it was the last thing to disappear below the water at night when the creature retired to bed—and death, because to kill its prey before eating it struck it with its tail.

Its head and eyes, for the same reason, represented light and day, etc.

The serpent was a representation of regeneration, because it changed its skin and became, so to speak, a new serpent.

SPIRIT WORSHIP IS OF TWO KINDS

1st. *The so-called Spirit Worship of elementary forces, or the propitiation of elementary spirits or powers,* arose in the mind of man when he observed the various powers and attributes of the forces of nature—water flowing—trees growing—darkness and light, and all associated with it—the heavens as the Great Weeper, and light which was considered the source of life to man and all else. From these powers of nature man would imbibe his Spiritual ideas, and so would lay the foundation or the beginnings of the later myths. Each at first was given and recognised by a sign and symbol; and afterwards a name would be attached or connected with each power or attribute—and one greater than all would become *The One Great Power or Spirit*, and the others would be attached as attributes or powers of The One.

You must be careful to distinguish these *spirits* or *powers*, from the second class, or *The Spirits of the Ancestors*, and the propitiation of these, which has been called Ancestral Worship, and is one of the typical leading features of the religion (or religious idea) of the Japanese of the present day.

This was the dawn of religion, because—

1. Religion proper commences with and must include the idea or desire for another life.

2. This belief in another life is founded on the resurrection of the Spirit.

3. The belief in the resurrection of the Spirit was founded upon the faculties of abnormal seership, which at one time led to Ancestor Worship in all lands.

4. It was a worship or propitiation of the Ancestral Spirits, *not of the body corpus*, which died and disintegrated.

The Egyptian religion was founded on the rising again of the human soul, emerging alive from the body of dead matter. The Corpus could not, and never did, come back, or make its appearance again in any form, but the Spirit that arose from this was visible to seers.

The seven elemental powers were afterwards, in the second exodus of the Nilotic Negro time, divinised and represented by seven gods ; at first two, Horus and Sut, then Shu, and, afterwards, the other five. There are two lists of these in the Ritual. To these were given stars on high ; later, they represented the seven Pole Stars, and were called *The Glorious Ones* in Stellar Mythos. The first three were the heroes, and play the great part in the folklore tales found all over the world. The old Earth Mother, Ta-Urt, was now divinised, and was represented as of both sexes and depicted by the Egyptians as the Great Mother Apt, who gave birth to the heroes. So we have the *Heroes* and *Glorious Ones* of Manetho, as well as the *Glorified Spirits*, these last having once been man ; the former were mythical, and had not been nor ever could be human. The Glorified Spirits were the spirits of their ancestors who had lived here on earth; and risen again after the death of the corpus.

c

The Heroes and Glorious Ones were the Mythical Gods, or divinised elementary powers, who had never lived or reigned as man or woman and never could, and it is in the mixing of these, without understanding the gnosis, that Dr Wallis Budge, in all his works on this subject, has confounded these divinised elemental spirits and thinks that these were human. The Hindus and others have gone wrong in their decipherment of the Ritual of ancient Egypt, as also the Hebrew translators of the Bible when they mention that the " Sons of God saw the daughters of men that they were fair and they took them wives of all which they chose " (Genesis), and " the Sons of God came in unto the daughters of men and they bare children to them." The translator thus mixes the mythical gods with the human woman ! The worship and the propitiation of the Glorified Spirits is what is called *Ancestral Worship.*

It is in the religious part of man's brain on which the greatest stability of the past is photographed. Primitive man's occupation was principally taken up in two things—

1st. *Hunting—to obtain food.*

2nd. *Religious ceremonies*—the enacting over and over again, from generation to generation, those tenets, sacred to him, which his forefathers had taught and impressed upon him. He had no books or writings as we have. He used sacred signs and symbols common to all, and danced the history of the past in various forms and ceremonies which all understood ; so that if a stranger came to the camp he would be known whence he came by his dance.

They live by hunting and fishing. They use bows and poisoned arrows and little spears and clubs.

They are a palæolithic nomad race, living in groups and passing from one place to another—the greatest and the first hunters, which fact Professor Sollas in his recent work has ignored altogether.

They fashion stone, flint, quartz and bamboo into knives ; and some tribes make nets, also primitive boats, by tying together bundles of papyri in lots of three, etc.

Some use the nose stick, others do not.

They have no Totemic rites or Totemic ceremonies; but they have dances in which they dance in Sign Language the ideas and beliefs which their limited monosyllabic language cannot express.

Thus we see that they are not a degenerate but the primary race.

1. They propitiate elementary powers.
2. They believe in a life hereafter.
3. They believe in a Great Spirit.
4. They have no magic.

The Bushmen are very little removed from the Pygmies, and, in fact, claim to be " first cousins." There are many features to prove that they are the next type in evolution, and after them the Masaba Negro.

They have in common :

1. The same peculiar odour as the Pygmy, different from that of the Negro.
2. Projection of the jaws and lips.
5. Flatness of the nose and its characteristic broadness at tip and root.
4. Lobeless ears—ill-defined.
5. Elongation of the palate.
6. Large size of teeth for such little people.
7. The same characteristic discrete peppercorn hair.
8. A primary monosyllabic language.
9. They are not Totemic and have no Totemic ceremonies, but have Sign Language and Sign Dances. They show the same skill in dancing as the Pygmy. This the Negro does not possess to the same degree; having

more articulate words to express his meaning, he would discontinue the habit of dancing the object, etc., intended to be conveyed.

10. They have the same convexity of the subnasal space.

11. Occasionally, and mostly in young women, steatopygia — greatly developed gluteal region — caused by the primitive mode of copulation practised, which fashion was changed by the Nilotic Negro.

12. Many words are identical.

13. Their sacred signs and ceremonies are the same ; they propitiate elementary powers and believe in after-life and the Spiritual World.

14. They have long forearm and large colon.

15. They live the same kind of nomad life as the Pygmy, but are bigger in stature, and have more developed religious ideas and mythical beliefs than the Pygmy.

The next after in evolution is the Masaba Negro, the men with strongly projecting superciliary arches, low brows, flat noses like the Pygmy, etc. From these followed the evolution of the Nilotic Negro.

Now, the Nilotic Negro, who possessed To-temic ceremonies, was the next man that left

Africa and followed the Pygmy throughout the world, and he is a peculiar type distinct from what is commonly understood as the true Negro.

The children of these Nilotic Negroes at birth are red or copper-coloured, but gradually darken, and the adult assumes a chocolate colour, which in some tribes, exposed to certain climatic conditions, is still darker. The children all have the very protuberant stomach of their ancestors the Pygmies; later on this is not so noticeable. Until about twenty to twenty-five the upper lip projects beyond the lower, as in the Pygmy; in later years the lower one projects more and more.

There is very considerable difference in the hair; in some it is wavy or curly, in some cases it is very distinctly curly or frizzled, *but never woolly or kinky as in the true Negro,* although the casual observer would be very likely to describe it as such.

Their noses are very depressed at the root, the supraborital ridges are strongly marked. But still more prominent is the great proportionate width of the nose; in some cases, as in the Pygmy, its breadth is more than its length, and the end is flattened. When they wear the nose stick it renders the alæ still wider, of course.

Between the Pygmy and the Nilotic Negro there is a fairly wide difference of evolution which is filled up by the Bushman and Masaba Negro. These two types are the connecting links in every way and on every point.

And I will just say here that the Nilotic Negro left old Egypt and followed the Pygmy throughout the world, driving him in front and away to inaccessible regions, where the Nilotic Negro could not or did not follow. I will return to the Nilotic Negro later, but wish to emphasise these points.

1. *The Pygmies were the first men that went out from Africa.*

2. *They are still found all over the world.*

3. *The Nilotic Negroes were the race that followed, and are still found all over the world, as I shall prove to you.*

4. *The Bushman and Masaba Negro, the connecting links, never left Africa, and cannot be found in any other part of the world, but they are still found in Africa.*

The reason for this is—

Because, *as some of the Pygmies travelled south,* in evolution they further developed into the Bushman, spread over South Africa, but could not get beyond on account of the sea. So the Bushman remained here, where we find him to-day—and if he had attempted to go north he would have found that evolution had taken place to the Masaba Negro and further to the Nilotic Negro, and would have been driven back again south and kept there, and the same with the Masaba Negro. The Nilotic people, who as they developed travelled farther north, were taller, stronger and more developed on every point, and would not allow these to come north of this, but drove them back south.

The true Negroes, as you understand them, never left Africa at all, until they were exported as slaves.

The Bushman and Pygmy do not fight each other, but the Nilotic Negro kills all the Bushmen and Pygmies he can.

Now, having given you proof that the Pygmy was the first man and that his home was inner Africa; let us see what evidence we have of his great antiquity.

I am pleased to see, from recent extracts and articles, that Professor Keith has also arrived at the conclusion that man must have existed on the earth over 750,000 years ago. But what does he mean by this statement, "that the *glacial period extended through hundreds of thousands of years in Europe* "?

Professor Sollas, Professor of Geology, Oxford, F.R.S.; etc.; states (ch. i. in his recent book, "Ancient Hunters and their Modern Representatives")—*That the world is now as it has always been, as regards man and his past history. The Quaternary cannot have exceeded some* 300,000 *or* 400,000 *years, during which period there have been four glacial epochs, one of which was of much longer duration than the rest—the Great Ice Age. The recent existence of a Great Ice Age was discovered by Schimper* (? !).

So Professors Sollas, Schimper and Keith ignore the Sun's revolutions around its centre and the Precession of the Pole Stars. If one believed what they have written, there could be no other explanation of this question but that the Sun and Pole Stars had taken a fit into their head and gone for a prolonged holiday, after which they returned to their ordinary routine again ! ! Can anyone for a moment suppose that such a thing could have taken place ? It is simply preposterous. Professor Sollas' " four complete oscillations " were four different glacial epochs.

The old Egyptian Wise Men kept the time

and marked down every stage, and have left records of the same, for at least ten glacial epochs. But although I have studied all the records that I have been able to find, there is no mention that the Sun or Pole Stars ever went for a holiday; and the Egyptians recorded time and the revolution of these for over 250,000 years, up to the end of the Stellar Mythos, and have left the fact recorded.

The arguments, conclusions arrived at, and imaginations of some geologists have apparently never taken into account that the Sun travels round its centre once in every 25,827 years, this forming "The One Great Year," and that during that period the Northern Hemisphere is frozen down to 56 latitude for part of the time. There is a Great Summer, Great Autumn, Great Winter and Great Spring in the Sun's year as in our year of 365 days. It would be useless to enter into any argument when the above has not been taken into consideration. That the glacial period recurs every 25,827 years is a sufficient argument and proof of all that we find, and will explain the differences and the causes of the bone of contention amongst geologists.

There is no proof, in my opinion, that the North of Europe was submerged under the sea. The amount of ice and snow which must have fallen in the North would be sufficient to carry the huge boulders we find in some parts of Europe away from their parent rock, such as we find, on a smaller scale, in the glaciers which are melting and travelling along or receding at the present day. The *boulder* alone remains, and the evidence of the sea-bed is not there. The form of the mountains in Norway and Sweden alone are sufficient proof that they have not been submerged and upheaved, as we find in the Australian continent.

In his Chapter II., p. 29, Professor Sollas states : " The dawn of the human race is supposed to belong to a past more remote than the beginning of the Great Ice Age ; yet of the existence of man antecedent to that epoch not a vestige of evidence forcible enough to compel universal belief " has up to the present time been discovered. I do not know what may be the standard of his " evidence forcible enough to compel universal belief," but we have the remains of a human skeleton found a mile north of Ipswich, beneath the Boulder Clay, in the glacial sands. The Boulder Clay was formed by the retreat of the Ice Sheet, and therefore these remains are distinct evidence that man lived here before the last two glacial periods. We have the remains of a human found eighty feet beneath a bed formed by running water in Germany — the skull found at Gibraltar—and others. We have the fact that the Osirian Cult which was *Solar Mythos* was at its perfection at Abydos 15,000 to 20,000 years ago, and that it existed in Heliopolis and other nomes before Abydos was built. We have the fact that Manetho stated that the Great Pyramids were built by the followers of Horus during the Stellar Mythos, which existed before the Lunar or Solar Cults. We have the fact that the Egyptian Priests had recorded the time of the Sun's revolution and the Precession of the Pole Stars for over 258,000 years, up to the Stellar Mythos. We have the fact that the Sun makes its revolution once in 25,827 years, during which time we have one Great Ice Age or Glacial Epoch ; and, in my opinion, we find definite implements of man in the Tertiary formation. Can Professor Sollas say that all the above was formed 26,000 years ago only ? If the above facts are not sufficient " to compel universal belief," then, as far as science is concerned, the present humans will still continue to wallow in the mire of ignorance, as they have in the dark and degenerate age we have passed through, since the downfall of the old Egyptian Empire.

This Glacial Epoch occurs in the whole of the Northern Hemisphere (Europe, Asia and North America) as well as in the Southern : how could the origin of man be in Asia ? He could never have worked out his Astro Mythology in Asia, when the whole of this was frozen and covered with ice down to the latitude of the South of France.

Nor could he do so if we placed his original home where Haeckel and his followers have placed it—namely, from a centre which influenced Egypt and Babylonia in the West, and America in the East—a centre in close proximity to Polynesia and Java. This will not bear critical examination after all the proofs to the contrary that I bring forward.

Haeckel could not take the observation day after day, month after month, and year after year, of the precession of the heavenly bodies as the old Egyptians did ; the climate would not allow this, where you have the whole of the heavens obscured for weeks at a time, during the rainy season. And the Egyptians have left records showing how patiently they must have worked for 250,000 years, proving that their observations were continuous and accurate.

Then again—although the Pygmies, also the Nilotic Negro, are in this part of the world, the connecting links of the Bushmen and Masaba Negroes are not here, neither is the true Negro. As a Glacial Epoch occurred, so man (who had gone North) would be driven back South; and as the epoch passed away he would go North again. Only in this way can any geologist give a definite and final answer to what he finds, and in this way alone—ever remembering that Old Egypt was sending out men more developed in mind and body with each exodus.

Professor Sollas' division of the human *by his three different kinds of hair* would be most amusing if he was not a professor at Oxford ; as he is, it is very, very sad to see such statements. But then the present anthropologists follow the same line of thought, and so one cannot be surprised.

He divides the humans thus into three groups :

1st. One in which the hair is without any twist—that is, it is perfectly straight.

2nd. That in which it is twisted to an

extreme, as in the Negro or Bushman (who are two quite different classes).

3rd. Those in which the hair is only twisted enough to be wavy, as in many Europeans. He finishes up with this remark—" The Tasmanians, like the Negro and most other races with dark skins, all belong to the same race or class."

He never mentions anything about the *difference in section of hair.* Compare the Australian's with the European's; then make a section of these, and tell me where Professor Sollas finds the missing link. Let him make a section of the Pygmy's; and then, comparing it with that of the Chinese and Japanese, tell me where he finds the missing link.

He evidently does not know that an existence in a cold climate for prolonged periods produces straight, coarse hair. If he took a section of the straight hair of the Eskimo and American Indians, could he tell me where he would find any to correspond ? I think not—but the same hair would be found in all the Nilotic Negroes, these including the Australian Ainu, the Eskimo, the North and South American Indians, as well as the Nilotic Negro in Africa.

The hair of the Chinese and Japanese and all the earlier Stellar Mythos people is different in higher formation, and that of the White Race still more different.

Then he is entirely wrong in his description of the character of those he quotes. *The Tasmanian and Pygmy race have a discrete peppercorn hair.*

The Nilotic Negro has not—it is frizzy and curly, some of it almost straight ; and that of the true Negro, who never left Africa, and came after and was evolved from the Masaba Negro in Africa, may be described as woolly or *kinky,* and quite different from that of the Pygmy or Nilotic Negro.

Nearly all the Nilotic Negroes, who travelled north during the past thousands of years, except the Ainu, have developed a straight hair ; some of these are frizzy or curly, but the climate accounts for the change that has taken place.

Professor Sollas takes the Tasmanians as the oldest people (ch. iv.), and states that they may be called " Eolithic." Well, at any rate, they are Palæolithic, and that is about all that is true of his ideas about them. *He classes them with the Negroes !* which they are not, and never were. *He also states that the cranial capacity is the lowest of any humans. This is also absolutely wrong. Their cranial capacity averages 1199 c.c.; the Pygmies have a cranial capacity of 900 c.c. average—difference nearly 300 c.c.*

These originally inhabited Australia, but were driven out by the Nilotic Negro and crossed over to Tasmania, where the Nilotic Negro did not follow them. These were a highly developed Pygmy.

The Tasmanian was a highly developed Pygmy in every sense of the word, a class of the human evidently unknown to Professor Sollas, as he never mentions them as such, although they were the first and greatest hunters.

Their hair was discrete peppercorn. From the evidence left, they had no Totems or Totemic ceremonies. They used the primitive club and spear of wood. They had rudely chipped stone implements for knives—viz., scrapers—and had not advanced to the stage of the Nilotic Negro (Australians) of hafting a stone on to a stick, but held the stone in the hand.

Their stone instruments are of the same Palæolithic form that one finds all over the world , they are the Pygmy implements,

D

and classed by geologists as plateau implements.

Ancient Implements.—The oldest evidence of man's existence on the earth are his implements.

These were *very primitive at first*—some of them probably only just a big stone, a broken piece of flint, or a piece of quartz; then flints rudely chipped into flakes, scrapers, etc., to which the geologists give the name of *the plateau instruments*, because they are found in gravels capping the high plateaux of Kent and elsewhere.

These are the implements of our forefathers the Pygmies.

Then there is a further development, where we find these flints flaked roughly on the sides and hafted into sticks, thus forming a primitive axe.

These were and are the implements of the Nilotic Negro race who followed and drove out the Pygmy.

Then in the next stage we find an advancement, a higher perfection in the formation of their instruments. I wish to draw your particular attention to these, because they are very important :

The Chillean industry instruments. In

these examples the flint or quartz is flaked off on each side, so as to form a kind of stone knife with a double edge.

These are found nearly all over the world— in Africa, Asia, Europe, and North and South America, with the following exceptions :— *Australia, Tasmania, extreme South America (and Oceania?).* This very important fact is specially to be noted, because of the absence of instruments where these Pygmies and Totemic people still are to be found. *It shows that the Chillean knives were associated first with the earliest Stellar Mythos people, who never reached Australia and Tasmania. So that even here in the later Tertiary and early Quaternary periods we have evidence, geologically, of how the different races of our forefathers travelled over the world, proved by extant tribes of the present day— namely, in Australia, New Guinea, New Hebrides.*

Now; although we have not found any remains of the osteo-anatomy of man below the Quaternary Period, we have found some of his implements—eoliths—flint knives and scrapers ; these would not perish, whilst his osteo-anatomy would disintegrate or decompose. Therefore we must take this as objective evidence that the human race existed so long ago as the Tertiary Age.

Professor Sollas has mixed all these tribes up together and calls them Negroes. They certainly are all Palæolithic ; but they represent different peoples and wide stages in the evolution of man, which Professor Sollas does not differentiate. Nor can he do so without taking the evolution of the cults and their anatomical condition into consideration, which idea he appears to scorn.

The plateau instruments—and those that are made from a flake, with only one side chipped, and not hafted—belong to the Pygmy race. There are no Totemic ceremonies. They are pre-Totemic.

The further developed forms of those instruments, roughly flaked on both sides and hafted, belong to the Nilotic Negroes.

These have Totemic ceremonies, whilst the further developed Chillean belong to the Stellar Mythos people of the first exodus.

Thus the cults bear out and prove in a most remarkable and perfect way their co-relation with the geological records found.

I would wish to draw attention to the

beautiful illustrations of these in Professor Sollas' work. He has given pictographs of all these in their perfect and various forms.

We will now take into consideration the

BURIAL CUSTOMS

The burial customs, rites and ceremonies, from the remotest times, were founded on the faith that the departed still lived in the spirit. They were buried for rebirth. *The corpse was bound up in the thrice-bent position* in the fœtal likeness of the embryo in utero, and placed in the earth as in the mother's womb. It did not denote a resurrection of the body corpus—but was *symbolical of rebirth in spirit.*

In the Stellar Mythos many symbols of reproduction and resurrection were buried in the tombs as amulets, with fetish figures of a protecting power. Elaborate preparations for the spiritual rebirth were made, as we find at Harlyn Bay, in Cornwall, and (as discovered in 1907) at La Chapelle aux Saints.

The grave of one of the prehistoric men was found here in a cave—a shallow pit 1·85 metres in length, 1 metre in breadth, and about 30 cm. in depth. The body was lying from east to west. I have not found which way it faced, but I believe it was south. Around it were a great number of well-worked " mousterian " implements, fragments of ochre, broken bones, etc.

Professor Sollas states : " This was evidently a ceremonial interment, occupied by offerings of food and implements, for the use of the deceased in the Spirit World. It was almost with a shock of surprise that we discovered this well-known custom, and all this implies already in existence the last episode of the Great Ice Age." This was the interment of a Stellar Mythos man, a later type than the Nilotic Negro. In March 1909, another skeleton was discovered in the lower cave of the famous Moustier itself—that of a man about sixteen years of age, lying on his right side with face to the south ; the right arm bent under the head, and the left arm extended. Burnt bones and implements were deposited about the skull. Bouchers, carefully dressed on both sides and beautifully worked, were just within reach of his left hand. He was a Stellar Mythos man.

The sacrifices offered to the dead are made

to propitiate *the living spirit of the dead—not the corpus.*   It was a fear that the ghost might return and manifest displeasure or revenge— a dread of the spirit—that caused the propitiation.

Thus the foregoing evidence shows and proves that they were early Nilotic Negroes and Stellar Mythos people.

The *Stellar Mythos were divided into two periods.*—Those with their faces *to the south were the Stellar Mythos people* of the first 51,000 or 52,000 years, when Sut was the Primary God.

Those with their faces to the north were of later date, when Horus was the Primary God.

Now, having given you the *objective evidence* that the Pygmy was the first and oldest human, I must turn to the *subjective evidence,* and I will ask you not to treat it with that contempt and scorn that possesses our friend Professor Sollas.

As regards my chronology, I have given you objective proofs ; now let me turn to the subjective proofs that we find

1st *In the Ritual of Ancient Egypt.*

2nd *In the Egyptian History of the Creation of the World,* version B, and *in the Borgan Codex.*

From the monuments of Ancient Cities in

the Central States of America, we find the same record written—namely :

" *They covered up my eye after them with bushes* (or hairy net) *twice for ten great periods.*"

A period was one great year of 25,827 years. Ten periods, therefore, would be 258,270 years. This record was written during the Stellar Mythos time.

"They covered up my eye twice after them," would represent a period of 51,654 years that they had recorded time and the Precession of the Pole Stars before Horus came into being, leaving at that time 206,616 years that he had then been existent as the Great One.

" They covered up my eye twice " = 51,654 years represents the time that Set or Sut was the Primary God—El Shaddi of the Phœnicians; this is borne out by Chapter XXXII. of the Ritual. Sut or Set existed as Primary God, therefore, over 50,000 years before Horus came, and for two periods he was covered up, in their reckoning of time ; he was the " Hidden of the Khas."

This and the monumental evidence proves that the Stellar Mythos was first worked out in the Southern Hemisphere, as I have previously shown—that it existed at least over

51,000 years before it was transferred to the Northern, when Horus became the Primary God and took his place with all the attributes hitherto attached to Sut. So in reckoning our chronology we have :

1. Primitive man, the Pygmy, who travelled and lived all over the world, say	- 250,000 years
2. Totemic Sociology, the Nilotic Negroes following after the Pygmy through all lands	- 250,000 „
3. Sut { 51,654 years Stellar Mythos	- 258,270 „
4. Horus 206,616	———— 758,270 ys.
5. Lunar Mythos - - say 25,000 „	
6. Solar Mythos - - „ 35,000 „	62,000 ys.
7. Christians - - - „ 2,000 „	
	————
	820,270 ys.

This would give the lowest estimate, as it is not certain when the above quotation was written during the Stellar Mythos.

Geologists give from 300,000 to 400,000 years for the *Quaternary* and *Recent Periods*, and some think it is uncertain if man existed during the Tertiary Period; I fully believe he did. We should not expect to find any human remains in this strata, primitive man only buried the corpus a few inches under the earth, and this would soon disintegrate; but some of the " Eoliths " found in the Tertiary Strata are undoubtedly of human workmanship, and I would add at least another 100,000 years to the time of the Quaternary period.

Language.—How many distinct words the Pygmies have, I have not yet been able to ascertain accurately, because some of the articulate sounds are so accompanied by gesture signs, or Sign Language, that it is difficult to gauge whether they are distinctly primitive words, or a particular sound accompanied by a gesture sign, as Sign Language. But if not to be classed as distinct words, these sounds undoubtedly became words afterwards—for example, "fifee" or so-called hiss of a snake; the " su " for the goose, etc.

The Nilotic Negro's language I have been able to ascertain fairly well. The first exodus of these possess about 900 distinct words. The second exodus a few more.

These are all monosyllabic; they have no prefixes or suffixes, although some anthropologists and ethnologists have added these because they have not understood the gesture sign.

Walter E. Roth is amongst the number to whom we are indebted for much information, as he has always been an accurate observer, though without the gnosis of the cults or Sign Language, which is a great pity, because he has devoted much time and study to these people ; and he is trying to read without learning the alphabet first, and thus is quite unable to arrive at a true interpretation of all he sees and hears. I am the only person up to the present time who has published a list of the true Pygmy words or language.

All the Pygmies and Nilotic men, and probably the early Stellar people, were hunters from necessity, winning a precarious existence from the chase of wild beasts and the collection of food. Yet man was superior to all other created things in nature ; he could make fire and form clubs from sticks and stones. The Stellar Mythos people from being hunters became shepherds. They found that they could tame animals, also that wild plants could be grown. They first settled into camps or villages, generally on the hills, and surrounded these with ditches and mounds to keep off the wild animals, etc.

Therefore Palæolithic man must be divided into three distinct classes at least, both anatomically and by his primitive implements, as well as *non - Totemic* and *To-temic*.

The first and primary are the Pygmy race. *These are non-Totemic, have peculiar and distinct anatomical features*, and their implements are characterised by a very primitive form.

The Nilotic Negro race are also Palæolithic, *but they are Totemic*; and there are at least two distinct types of evolution in their Totemic ceremonies, the first without " Hero Cult," and the second with it, and anatomically one race is superior and higher in evolution than the other. Their implements show a great advance, not only in a higher art of manufacture, but also through their possession of the knowledge of making others that the primary race had not acquired. Their anatomical features prove also how much progress the human race had made in evolution up to this point.

Now the only man, except myself that I know of, who has observed the difference of these two types, is Dr Haddon, Reader of Ethnology at Cambridge, who (I believe) was the head of an expedition that went out to Torres Straits. He has published the result of his observations in his reports of the

Cambridge Anthropological Expedition to Torres Straits. He has described distinctly the differences in a great many particulars of these two different exodes of the Nilotic Negro, and his observations are true and accurate.

If you make no distinction between these two exodes, you have missed the key with which to unlock the mysteries of the past. This is what all writers hitherto have done. I am certain that if Professor Sollas and other writers on this subject took into consideration the evolution of the Cults, with their anatomical and physiological conditions which they now treat with scorn, not only would these writers be able to trace the history of man on a firm and definite basis, but they would discover that their geological researches would agree critically on every point with it.

I will now draw your attention to the illustrations of the osteo remains found of primitive man and the various reconstructions of him that have been made, the sacred signs and symbols, etc.

SOME PYGMY WORDS

(*See* "Signs and Symbols of Primordial Man")

Pygmy	Egyptian Hieroglyphics		Equivalent in English
O-be		ànb	to dance, to rejoice
Mai		mu	water
A-do-da		āx or za	to sleep
Bacchaté		baak	grain, fruit, bread, food
Massouri		maau	good, right, to be good, to do well, to be straight
Tzi-ba		Xerpu-baa	a bow, a piece of wood, etc.

Pygmy	Equivalent in English
O-be	A dance
Maria-ba	Pipe of Bamboo to smoke
Tath-bà	Whistling into a reed
Oct-bà	Wood
Di-pé	Spear
A-do-da	Sleep
A-pé	Arrow
Tzi-ba	Bow
Mai	Water or drink
Massouri	Good, well
Kon-pé	Clothes of any nature
Ma-di	Hunting horn
La-gou-ma	Bristle head-dress
Kalli-Kélli	Native bell
Bacchaté	Bread. This word is sometimes used—macchaté, the "ch" hard
A-foie	Dagger

I am greatly indebted to Mr HUGH and Mr JOHN ALLEN for placing their beautiful collection of implements at my disposal. I have selected the following from their cabinets for illustration in this work.

MASABA NEGROES

I HAVE used the term " Masaba Negroes "
to denote those Prognathous types of the
human who were evolved from the true
Pygmy, and from whom developed the
Nilotic Negro to the N. and N.E., and the
true negro to the W. and S.W., and which
now exist under various names.

Dr Robinson, in his " Travels Through
Haussaland," remarks on the very ape-like
appearance of the wild mountainous tribes
in the Bauchi country north of the River
Benue.

Sir Harry Johnson also remarks upon these;
which he mixes sometimes with the Pygmies,
and although he classes them as somewhat
of a different type, he does not differentiate
the two.

We describe them as short of stature—
somewhat taller, however, than the Pygmy,
beetling-browed, prognathous, with long
bodies and short legs, long forearms, Pygmy

E   65

noses, long upper lips, colour dirty chocolate-brown, large abdomens.

Hair very much as the Pygmy peppercorn. Some have short, scrubby beards.

Most of them bore the upper lip with holes. They do not knock out their teeth. They practise circumcision in some cases.

At the present time these are met with all down Central Africa in groups and nomad tribes, from the Bahr-al-Ghazal to the upper waters of the Zambezi ; and westwards, from the Bahr-al-Ghazal to the Portuguese Guinea ; and may also be found at the present day between Lake Kewn and Lake Albert Edward on the East, and Congo Forest, countries west of Ruwenzori, mixing with the Bakonjo and Baamba Tribes, also to the west of Semliki River, on western slopes of Mount Elgon, in the vicinity of Lake Stephania, and in N.E. Africa, in the forests of Kiagwe, and amongst the nomad tribes of the Andorobo. They are called by other negro natives Banande or Munande.

The resemblance of these Masaba Negroes in West Elgon to the Congo Pygmies is very striking, and those of the N.E. Africa—the Doko—to those of the Andorobo.

They have bows and arrows and live to a

great extent on raw flesh, wild honey, bee-grubs, reptiles and bananas, when they can get these.

Osteologically they show a type between the Pygmy and Nilotic Negro. *"These people never left Africa."*

From these were developed the first Nilotic Negroes to the East, North and North-East of Africa. To the west the True Negro developed, climate and environment being the cause of differences in the different types that were evolved.

I will now show some of the sacred signs and symbols of these primitive people, which if you will use as I will now demonstrate, you can then go amongst them and be received as a brother. They will not injure you, but will give you all they can and protect you from harm.

The first is a 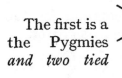 sacred sign amongst the Pygmies (*one upright stick and two tied across*), and signifies

their Great One—their Chief One. It was after carried on in the Stellar Myths and is one of the Ideographic symbols of Amsu—

i.e. the risen Horus—and still later amongst

the Christians
verted into the
it has been con-
double cross.

A still more sacred sign is this—a double triangle (1) surrounded and guarded by four serpents.   I have here one of the oldest

(1) 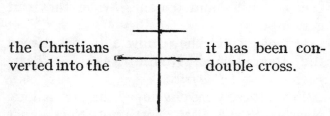 (2)

"Scarabs" in the world, with the above triangles and serpents on one side (1), and on the other (2) the representation of an island surrounded by water, and this at the outside with earth—*i.e.* their sacred island in a lake.   The earliest Ideograph for the Khui Land—or Land of the Spirits or Gods—

another and later form as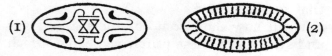

three triangles (double) surrounded by concentric circles.   The meaning is the same— one much older than the other.

When approaching these people take a green branch of a bush, or green leaves, and, holding them in the right hand, raise it above your head, as if to heaven, or, if you cannot get any bush or green thing, raise your hand with palm towards heaven. Amongst the Nilotic Negro tribes, who have the Hero Cult, raise your right arm with closed hand; except index finger, which should point to the Celestial North, or to Sothos, and then bring it, with a wide sweep, and point downwards. The indication is that the spirit goes down into the west, to the underworld, travels through this and comes up again as a white spirit in Sothos, in the east, and then travels to the Celestial North. Some give this sign —pointing to the west, sweep down and around and then bring the arm and finger up, pointing to the north. This, with crossing the arms on the breast, will carry you through all the tribes in North and South America, and all others that I know of. If you know the Sacred Totem—*i.e.* their Mother Totem— from which the tribes descended, and show this as well, after the above signs, you may ask for anything and nothing will be refused you.

Time will not permit me to go into the

meaning and origin of Totems and Totemic ceremonies. On a future occasion I shall be happy to trace the human where I now leave off—*i.e.* Nilotic Negro—through Totemic Sociology, Stellar, Lunar, and Solar Myths, and to the present generation. I will only give you here, as the last, the origin of "Totem." It is not American, as some have stated, but

Egyptian, and comes from Tem-tu ⋏⊠⋏, the

two halves—that is a moiety or division into two halves, and this is the ideograph for the same as can be seen in Bunson & Pierrot's Dictionaries.

I thank you for your attendance here to-night, and the kind attention you have paid to me, and I trust that I have not only interested you but given you proofs on "the Origin and Evolution of Primitive man" that you have not heard before, and which you will agree with me are conclusive evidence of my contention.

I give here the photograph of the skull found in one of the cists at Harlyn Bay, in Cornwall (with many thanks for permission to reproduce the same to Mr Reddie Mallett). This human was buried in the thrice-bent position facing North, and over the cist was a triangular stone with apex pointing north ; therefore a Stellar Mythos man, at the time that Horus I. was Primary God. The whole form and convolution of the cranium and jaws show a " modern man type." The position of burial proves him to be a Stellar Mythos man, and therefore he lived here before the Druids came to this country, who were Solar Mythos people, and after the Nilotic Negroes. He was here in Cornwall at the time and built those temples, the remains of which I found in the west of England, with *Two Circles*, representing the division of heaven in two divisions, North and South, and these were many thousand years older than those of the Three Circles (Solar Mythos), a good example of which may be seen at Rough Tor, in Cornwall, and represent the division of the heavens in *three twelves*—*i.e.* thirty-six divisions—and we can gauge the time by that of the division of Egypt into thirty-six nomes (see " Signs and Symbols of Primordial Man ").

Professor Keith appears not to understand—

(1) Why the existence of the tall Cromagnon race should have appeared and died out.

(2) Why the Neanderthal type have been found in a higher or more recently formed strata than the Ipswich and Galley Hill men, whom we may term modern men.

(3) Why the Tibia in the Ipswich man differs from the others that have been found, and

(4) Where the big brain type come from ?

These questions, and many others, can never be solved by our present geologists, anthropologists, or Professor Keith, as long as they continue to believe in the present fallacy which is still taught by the professors of Oxford, Cambridge, London and other great universities.

And yet the solutions of these questions are quite easy when you learn to read the true alphabet of the past.

The tall race of Europe, who came up from Egypt, were an exodus of the Turkana. These Nilotic Negroes are still found in Africa, a fine race of men, some of them over seven feet in height, very muscular and powerful, have high foreheads, large eyes, rather high cheek-bones, mouths not very

large and well shaped, lips rather full—
" The Cromagnon man of Europe." He was
followed by another race from Egypt, of
shorter stature, like the Ipswich man, and,
after, the Galley Hill man.

I cannot follow Professor Keith in his idea
of the differences found in the Tibia, being
any point to be taken into consideration of
the evolution of the human race, except the
posture they adopted in " sitting." Anyone
who will observe the different modes of
sitting, that these natives have adopted, must
feel that it cannot have any other effect upon
this bone than that which we find, and it has
that, if Professor Keith will examine the
bones of these living types, photograph of
which I here reproduce by kind permission
of ——. I am sure he will be as convinced
as I am (who have examined some of
them). But he has to take the typical
types: by this I mean, when from infancy
the tribe adopts this particular position.
He will find examples in Sir Harry
Johnson's book, " Uganda," as well as the
photographs I have given here, which must
convince him, as an anatomist, that the con-
stant strain and action of the different
muscles of the leg, in the posture adopted,
will produce the condition he finds.

We give here the photograph of two Nilotic Negroes (by kind permission of Sir H. Johnston and Messrs Hutchinson & Co.).

These are the extant representatives of the " big-headed " or " big-brained " people whose osteo remains have been found in Europe. As in the case of all other Nilotic Negroes, there was no progressive evolution of them outside Africa, and they died out in Europe and Asia, as a distinct race. The Turkana and Masai, who followed, although of a higher type anatomically and mentally, did not possess a larger cranium. I might here remark that the size of the head is not always the indicator of a clever man, or a clever race—it is the " grey matter," or amount of grey matter, which is the representative of clever men. You may have a large brain with the grey matter very " thin," and no depth in the " sulci," and another man with smaller brain, possessing greater depth of " sulci," and thicker grey matter. The latter man would be much the higher type of the two intellectually.

I give here three reconstructions by Trevor Haddon, R.B.A., under my direction, and I am greatly indebted to Mr Trevor Haddon for his patience and skill in reproducing all the details, as instructed, in such an elegant and accurate form as he has done in these.

(1st) A Reconstruction of Primary Man, (Pithecanthropos Erectus) found by Professor Du Bois in Java in 1890, over which there has been much discussion and differences in opinion. But undoubtedly this is part of the remains of primary man, and I quite agree with Professors Du Bois and Keith in their opinion that it is so. As further proof of what Professor Keith has already pointed out, I think the cranial capacity is critical evidence—viz. the .cranial capacity of this is 850 c.c., although Professor Keith says that this is probably too low an estimate. Now, the highest cranial capacity of any Anthropoid is 600 c.c. and the average Pygmy is 900 c.c. Therefore this would be the cranial capacity of a low type of Pygmy.

Professor Keith and others have never taken into consideration the cranial capacity of the Pygmies, which must be considered, these being the first "human" formed from the Anthropoid. I have placed his height as about four feet, but probably he was a little shorter.

(2nd) *A reconstruction of Neanderthal Man*
(by Trevor Haddon, R.B.A., under my
direction).

I give here a reconstruction of the
Neanderthal Man. Remains of him have
been found widely distributed over some
parts of Europe, but, up to the present time,
none have been brought to light in the
British Isles, Italy, America, or Asia proper,
although, as these remains form part of the
osteo-anatomy of those primary Nilotic
Negroes who first left old Egypt and followed
the Pygmies, it is possible such relics lie
hidden in these countries.

The type is still extant in Africa, and in Australia types of them may be found amongst
the Arunta tribes to the present day.

Although the remains have been found in a
more recent formation, geologically, than
those of the Galley Hill and Ipswich men,
yet the original prototype left old Egypt
thousands of years before the Galley Hill
man, and is lower in the scale of evolution.
It appears probable that the whole of Europe
and Asia were populated by this type imme-
diately after the extermination of the
Pygmies, whom they drove before them, as
in Australia.

The reason that we do not find their skeletons in the lower strata (Pliocene) is probably due to their burial customs, and disintegration. That we have found part of their skeletons in isolated places, in a more recent formation than other higher types of the human, who left old Egypt thousands of years after, is not surprising.

The primary, leaving their old home, would spread over Europe and Asia, travelling north, until driven back by a glacial period. They would then return south until the cold ice period had passed away, when they would again advance northwards.

How many times these migrations occurred before a higher race came up from old Egypt and fell upon these we cannot say, nor is it possible to form an accurate estimate of the time that must have elapsed before the type was extirpated—probably many hundreds of thousands of years. For these Neanderthal men would doubtless retreat from their enemies in isolated groups, and, when not molested, would propagate a true breed until the last man was extinct, except, of course, when they had taken the Pygmy women in marriage.

They would not be allowed to take the women of the superior race; the superior race, on the other hand, while exterminating the males, would take the females of the inferior race.

The implements found with the skeletons (or parts of skeletons), and also their cranial capacity and other features, prove them to be of a higher type in evolution than the Pygmy.

This is a representative instance of misjudging the type and class of man by the geological formation his remains have been found in, and in which Professor Keith, as well as Geologists and Anthropologists, have gone wrong in their deductions, from finding these osteo remains in a strata of more recent formation, than those remains found of a higher type of this human. The reason I have fully set forth under my " reconstructions."

In my forthcoming book, dealing with the Nilotic Negro and their evolution, all these points will be fully set forth.

(3rd) Reconstruction of the Ipswich Man (by Trevor Haddon, R.B.A., under my direction).

Probably this is the skeleton of a Nilotic Negro, but of a much later date, and higher in the scale of evolution than the Neanderthal man.

Besides Totems and Totemic ceremonies, this man would have " Hero Cult," whereas the Neanderthal man would not.

If this Ipswich man is a Nilotic Negro, it can be proved, not only by the worked flints found with, or near him, but also by his cranial capacity and burial position. He was buried in the thrice-bent position, but it has not been stated if he faced north or south, and I have not been able to obtain any photographs of the flint implements found near, as Mr Reid Moir, to whom I wrote, had none he could send me ; therefore, without these details I cannot positively say if this was a man of a late exodus of the Nilotic Negro, or one of an early exodus of Stellar Mythos.

Originals of this class are still extant in Africa and isles of the Pacific. He is an earlier type of homo than the Galley Hill man, whom we must classify as belonging to the Stellar Mythos period, from instruments found near him.

We can reckon 200,000 years at least, between the period of the Galley Hill man and that of the present time. The records mentioned before prove this.

Up to this period of evolution, these different types of humans did not develop one from another in Europe, Asia, or anywhere else, but in Africa. It was in Africa that evolution, from the first man—lowest in the scale—developed up to the Stellar Mythos people. As each type attained a higher standard, so exodes took place, the races migrating north, east and west.

In these early times, when no facilities existed for travel, the whole distances had to be traversed on foot, members of an exodus making their camps and homes secure as they went north, before another step in the advance could take place. At first they would travel along the easiest routes where plenty of food could be obtained, and would not trouble to attack the primary race so long as the latter did not interfere with their avocations. The Aborigines, retiring to mountains and forests where the invaders would not follow, would thus escape

F

annihilation, as witness, the Pygmies in New Guinea and other places at the present day.

It is my firm opinion that the reconstruction of all that we find can be fairly accurately made by taking into consideration, and comparing, the instruments, cranial capacity, and osteo-anatomy with those of still extant tribes found in various parts of the world.

I cannot let Professor Keith's statement pass without the greatest protest, namely— "The Galley Hill man, who is one of the modern build of body, *lived in England long before the Neanderthal man lived in France and Central Europe.*"

The Neanderthal man was in Europe probably over 300,000 years before the Galley Hill man was in England. The reasons and proofs I have shown.

He was evolved from the Masaba Negro, and was the first type of Nilotic Negro that left old Egypt, whereas the Galley Hill man is a Stellar Mythos man, and certainly 300,000 years later in time of evolution.

Professor Keith thinks that this branch of the human, Neanderthal type, might have sprung from the Gorilla, and that the others from the Gibbon, on account of the great difference in the Osteo-Anatomy found in this primitive man—but why ?   Does he suppose that a cart-horse and a thorough-bred horse were evolved from the same original, or from two different sources ? ? ?

To me his statements (supra) are as absurd as Sir Harry Johnson's ("The Uganda Protectorate," page 474) where he states : " Because white races may have arisen twice or thrice or four times independently from Mongol, Negro, and the Neanderthal-Australoid type " ! ! !

Then, from whence did they come, and how evolved ?   And what facts can he bring forward for such a theory ?   None. Such a statement is too unscientific for any argument or consideration.   Sir Harry Johnson's use of the term " Bantu " is also very misleading, and, in my opinion, quite wrong in every way, because under this term he mixes some Masaba Negroes, Nilotic Negroes and true Negroes all together, whereas there is a wide difference in time of evolution, and here I quite agree with the late Sir H. M. Stanley.

No one could ever follow the true evolution of the human race by his ideas as set forth in his book, " The Uganda Protectorate."

Even in his ideas of the " Bantu Language "

(page 892) and the origin of this, for instance.

The oldest prefixes, as he calls them, " Mu," " Ma " and " Nga " *are Pygmy words*, and rendered in the old Egyptian hieroglyphic language by the Ideographs as proof of this, namely, 〜〜 and 〜〜, etc. Most of his prefixes were original Pygmy words and *have been brought on in Negro languages.* Ideographs with prefixes and suffixes were added in later languages—for example ╝

Ba or Bu, Pa or Pu, Sa or

Su 〜〜 Mu or Mua, and 〜〜 Nga (this is a very difficult sound to pronounce as the Pygmies pronounce it. The Greeks could not do so, and changed it into Ch). These are some of the original Pygmy words, the first articulate words of man, and arise from the observation of the sounds made by the water running, the goose hissing, the duck in flight and the Ba or Bu of an animal like the sheep. I might add many others. These words then became the name of the subjects or objects as expressed by the sounds emitted, and this was the origin of language. Their Ideographic signs were expressive of syllables, and no syllabary can be found from which the vowel sounds are absent. There could be no reason for it—these were the originals which have never been taken into account by philologists. Signs preceded words. Words preceded writings.

	Formations	Periods	Types of Man
	Alluvial	Historic and Neolithic Flints	Modern and Barrowmen
Pliestocene	Buried Channel of Thames Lowest Terrace	Magdalenian Solutrean Aurignacian	Cromagnon Combe-Chapelle Grunaldi
	4th Glacial 30 Foot Terrace	Mousterian	Neanderthal Spy, La Chapelle, La Quna, Jersey
	3rd Glacial 100 Foot Terrace	Acheulian Chellean	Bury St Edmunds, Moulin Quinon, Dennise, Grenville, Gallery Hill
	Boulder Clay 2nd Glacial	Worked Flints	Ipswich
	Mid Glacial Contorted Drift Cromer Beds Norwich Beds Plateau Drift	Worked Flints	Llandudno Foxhall Heidelberg (Nilotic Negro) [1]
	1st Glacial Lenham Beds Red Crag Series	Worked Flints	Pithecanthropus (Pygmy) [1]
Pliocene	Coralline Crag Series	Worked Flints	Casteuldoloman (Calaveras)

The above is a supposed Geological Chart showing the probable sequence of strata formed in England during the recent Pliestocene and Pliocene Periods which our present geologists have divided into four glacial epochs, and as each glacial epoch occurs during every 25,827 years, all this would have been formed during 103,308 years, an utterly absurd and preposterous supposition, especially when we have the fact recorded still extant that the Stellar Mythos people (those who first kept time and reckoned it by the revolution or precession of the Pole Stars; Ursa Minor or Little Bear) had kept and recorded *ten such cycles during Stellar Mythos alone—i.e. 258,270 years.* This was after the Nilotic Negroes, Masaba Negroes, Bushmen and Pygmies had come into existence, and before Lunar and Solar Mythos and Christianity.

[1] Author's Notes.

1ST HOMO

AFRICAN PYGMY. (Hunters only)

West	North and East	South

Masaba Negroes

(Hunters only)

Masaba Negroes
Never left Africa—still here   (Non-agricultural)

Bushmen | Tribes
Hunters | Only
Hottentot Tribes

Never left Africa—still here—
did not develop into higher
types.

West

North-West, North and East, North-East

Mananbe
Babira
Babuku
Baamba
and others

Balega, Banchi, Bakonjon, Bande, Doko, Munande,
or Mibira, Mnyanwezi and others

Developed into true Negroes
which never left Africa—
still here—have not evol-
ved into higher types.
(Agricultural)

These developed into Nilotic Negroes. (Some agricultural)

Andorobo, Lendu, Toro, Bakonjo, Shiluk, Dinka, Nuer, Shangala, Niam-Niam,
Chir Mandari, Janbara Dyur (Luo) Madi, Aluru Acholi (Shuli) Lango, Umiro,
Kumum, Jardum Ja-luo (Kavirondo tribes) and many other minor tribes.

Exodes of these took place to
all parts of the world and
followed the Pygmy.

Bari, Nandi, Suka, Turkana

From these developed the

Highly developed Nilotic
Negroes who (developed
from the Bahima) worked
out the Stellar Mythos and
who spread oversome parts
of the world—viz., Europe,
Asia, America (except ex-
treme South) but did not
go to Oceania.

Nyemprians

Bachwezi, Bairo, Bahima

Masai. (Ancient Egyptians)

Somali and Galla

Mongoloids and Tibetians. (Stellar Mythos people)

Stellar Mythos. (Ancient Egyptians) monumental

Lunar } Mythos   (Ancient Egyptians)
Solar } Mythos

These went over all Europe, except extreme north, part of Asia,
but not north of Japan, nor Oceania. In America only the
Mayas, and south as far as Peru, not north ; or east of the
Andes, as far as can be discerned at present.

Christian Cops

Europe	Asia	Africa	+	America	+	Oceania

PYGMY. Evolved in Africa

Exodes went out all over the World

AFRICAN PYGMY	Europe	America	Asia	Oceania
Developed into Masaba Negroes and Bushmen, only found in Africa. Masaba Negro developed into the	Died out	Existing in South America	Existing here	Still existing here
Nilotic Negroes. An exodus of Nilotic Negroes all over the world. Took place after the Pygmy.	No progressive evolution from these, they will all die out			
Africa—still existing—and these developed into the	Died out	Still existing	Still existing	Still existing
Monumental Egyptians, Masai and Turkana and Suk, Bahima, Somali and the Gala.	No progressive evolution from these outside Africa; some may have married Pygmy women, and the later exodus men married the women of the primary exodus			
Stellar Mythos people. Earliest Tibetians and Mongoloids. Types are still extant in South America.	Died out. Giving place to the Solar Mythos people	Representatives still exist	Still exist	None—did not come here
Developed into Lunar and then Solar Mythos people	Married and inter-married and some development in evolution took place as the white race came into existence during this period—offshoots from the yellow—with inter-marriage and climatic conditions would account for the change.			
Ancient Egypt at its Zenith				
Solar Mythos people	Died out as Solar Mythos people, and Christians took the place of Solar Mythos	Types — Mayas in Mexico and South America in Peru. Never in North America (or South of Peru) or East of the Andes	Still exist	None
Ancient Egypt in decay and degeneration				
Christian Copts				
Christians. Africa	Europe	America	Asia	Oceania

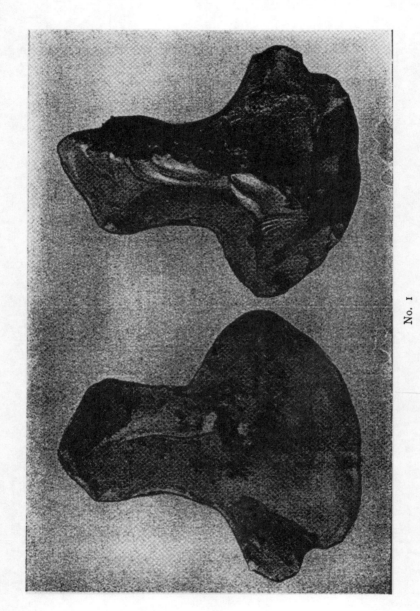

No. 1

PALEOLITHIC

Pygmy implements, chipped on one side only.

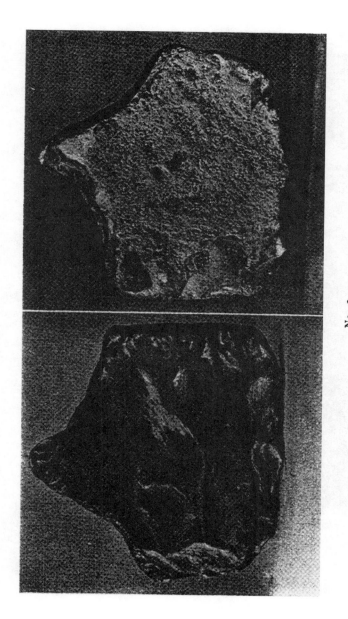

No. 2

PALEOLITHIC

Pygmy implements, chipped on one side only.

No. 3

PALEOLITHIC

Pygmy implements, chipped on one side only.

No. 4

PALEOLITHIC

Nilotic Negro instruments, chipped and worked on both sides roughly, found all over the world and associated with the Totemic people—*i.e.* those that have Totemic Ceremonies.

No. 5

PALEOLITHIC

Nilotic Negro instruments, chipped and worked roughly on both sides.

No. 6

PALEOLITHIC

Nilotic Negro instruments of the latter exodus, flaked off, chipped, and worked
on both sides, somewhat roughly, but showing a great advance on the primary
rough work of the first exodus.

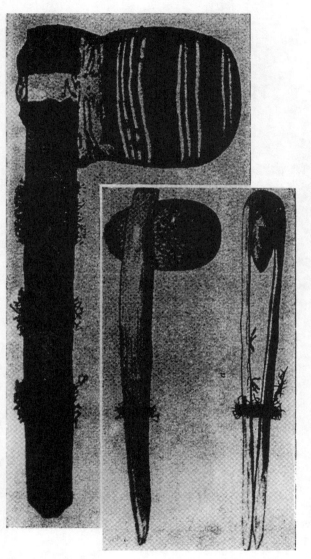

No. 7

PALEOLITHIC. NILOTIC NEGROES

Method of hafting an axe
Warramunga Tribe.

Showing mode of hafting a decorated
line ornament.

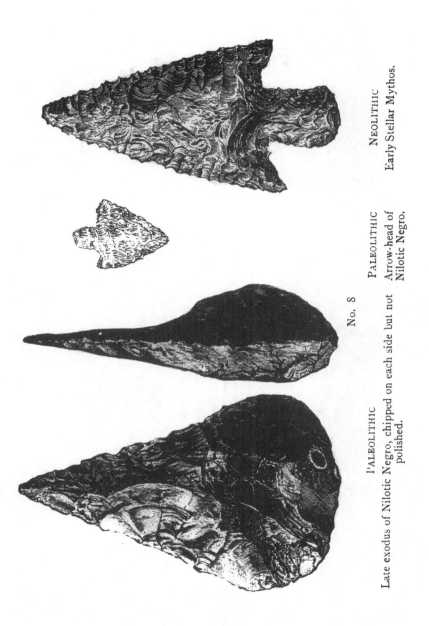

NEOLITHIC
Early Stellar Mythos.

PALEOLITHIC
Arrow-head of
Nilotic Negro.

No. 8

PALEOLITHIC
Late exodus of Nilotic Negro, chipped on each side but not
polished.

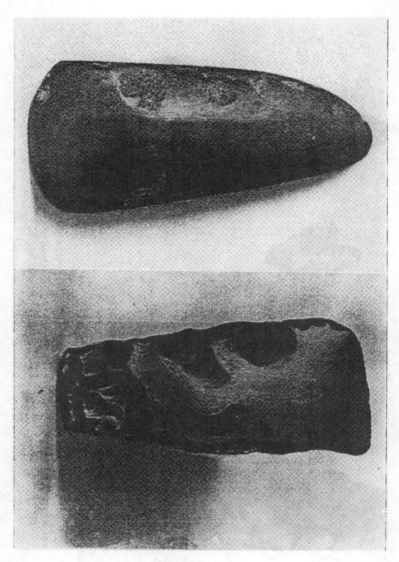

No. 9

IMPLEMENTS OF THE STELLAR MYTHOS PEOPLE OF THE FIRST EXODUS

These are flaked, chipped, and fashioned on each side, some very beautifully, into knives, spear-heads, arrow-heads, etc., and are only found in Europe, Africa, Asia, and some parts of Central, North, and South America. *They are not found* in Australia, Tasmania or Oceania and are only associated with the Stellar Mythos people, who never went to these latter countries. But I am of the opinion that these will be found in Java and the Caroline Islands as there are other remains, and proofs that these people went there.

H

Length	.	.	.	$9\frac{1}{2}$ inches
Width	.	.	.	2 ,,
Thickness	.	.	.	$\frac{3}{8}$ of an inch

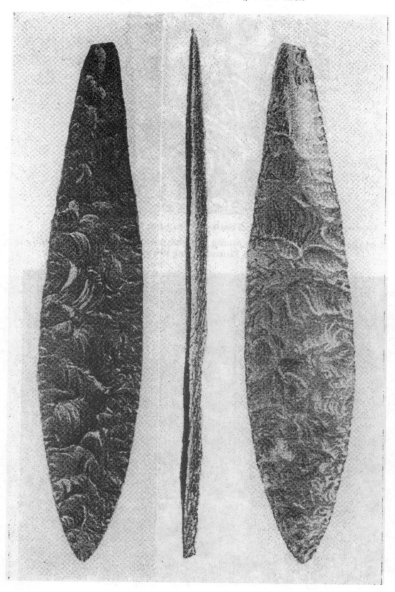

No. 10

NEOLITHIC. STELLAR MYTHOS PEOPLE

The most perfect and beautiful specimen I have seen of flint dagger or large double-edged knife, beautifully worked on each side and polished. The above illustration represents each side, and the edge is portrayed in the central figure.

EGYPTIAN PREHISTORIC TOMB. STELLAR MYTHOS MAN

Buried in the thrice-bent position facing **N.** with many amulets around him.
Time during which Horus I. was primary God.

No. 11

STELLAR MYTHOS MAN

Found buried in thrice-bent position in cist at Harlyn Bay, Cornwall, facing N.,
therefore at time Horus I. was primary God.

No. 72

Found at Uxmal, Yucatan, body buried in thrice-bent position, but it has not been stated for certain if this faced North or South : if South, then he was buried at the time Sut was primary God—before Horus I.

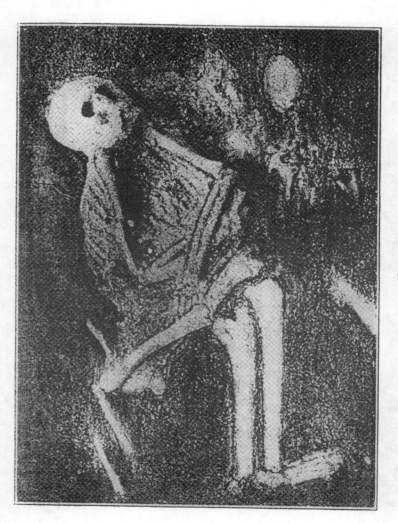

No. 13

Stellar Mythos man found buried in cist at Harlyn Bay, Cornwall. Thrice-bent position facing North, therefore time of Horus I.

No. 14
Pygmies showing characteristic hair, nose, lips, etc.

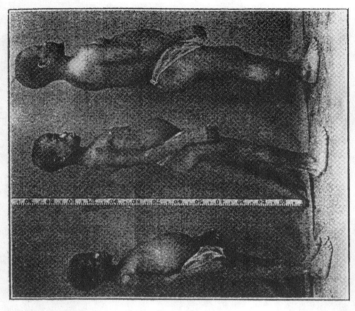

Pygmies showing height and general frontal appearance.
Note long forearm in central figure particularly.

No. 15

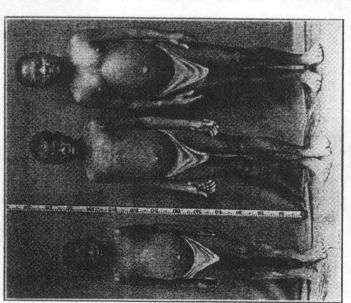

Pygmies showing large abdomen and height.

No. 16 General frontal appearance—two women and one man.

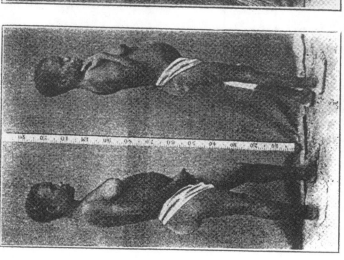

Pygmies—Side view, two women. Note Steatopygia in figure on left.

No. 17

Tasmanian Natives, who were highly developed Pygmies.
Note lips, nose, peppercorn hair, etc.

No. 18

THE GOD BES

The first god anthropomorphically depicted : it is the primitive human form of Horus I., Bes-Horus being the earliest type of the Pygmy Ptah. The human type was not given to any before Ptah, so that the above shows that the ancient Egyptians left an indelible proof in their mythology of their descent from the first human, who was the Pygmy.

No. 19

Bushman, showing Pygmy hair, lips, nose, etc.

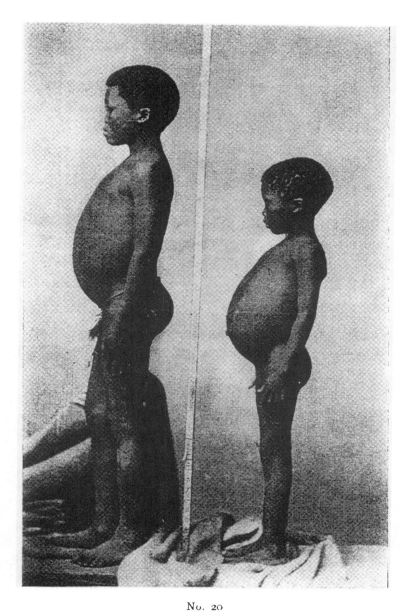

No. 20

Bushmen, showing large abdomen, peppercorn hair, depressed nose, and long forearm.

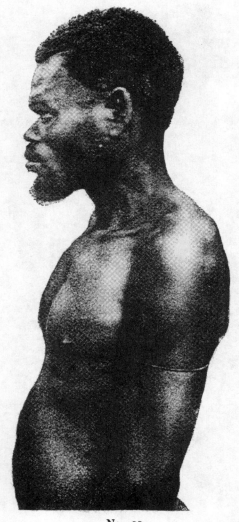

No. 21

Masaba Negro—Profile.

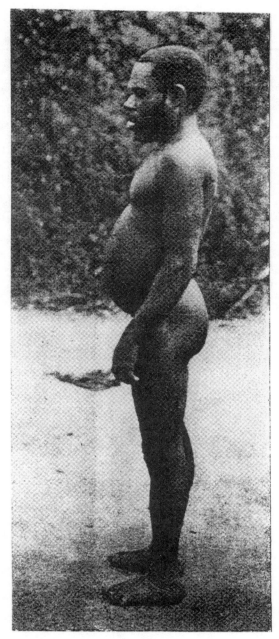

No. 22

Masaba Negro, showing long forearm

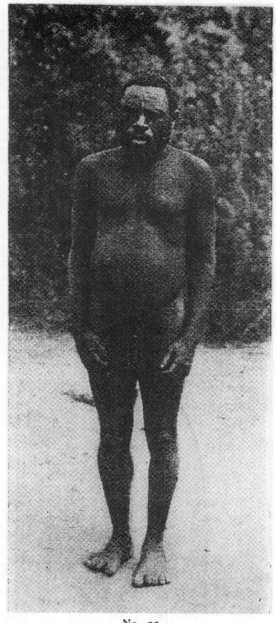

No. 23

Masaba Negro—Full face, showing Pygmy lips, long
forearm, and large abdomen.

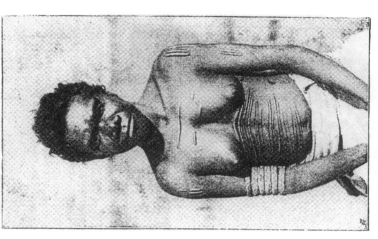

No. 24

Nilotic Negro children, showing large abdomen of the Pygmy in childhood which disappears in later life.

Front face, showing the early characteristic lips of the Nilotic Negro which I call Pygmoid.

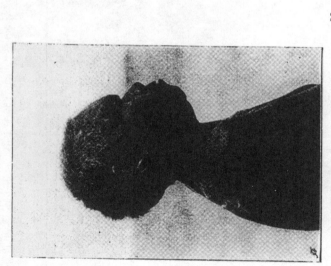

Nilotic Negro, showing the projection of lower lip in old age.

No. 25

A girl of the Nilotic Negro, showing the upper lip projecting over the lower in earlier life—until about 20-25; after, the lower lip projects the most.

Nilotic Negro, showing Pygmy upper lip and nose in young woman, and the change that has taken place in the old, as development in the progressive change of evolution of the human—also with the hair no longer Pygmy but curly and fuzzy.

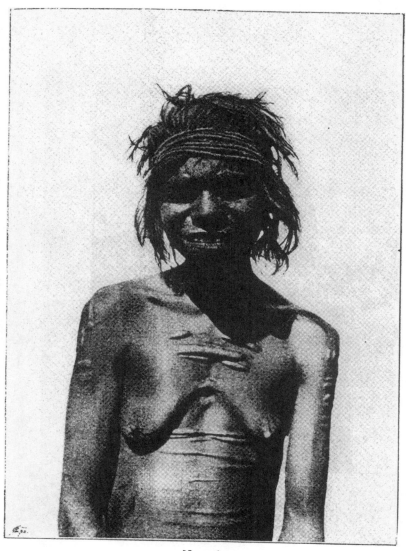

No. 26

TYPE OF FIRST EXODUS OF NILOTIC NEGRO
Note Pygmy nose, lips, also the incisor tooth knocked out, and the hair tied up.
Note also cicatrisation—no tattoo.   No Hero-cult.

No. 27

A man of the first exodus of the Nilotic Negro, showing Pygmy nose. He has Pygmy lips early in life, which change later—a Neanderthal type of man. Shows cicatrisation all over front of body. No Hero-cult.

Side View of Nilotic Negro

Showing prominent ridge above eyes, curly hair, etc.

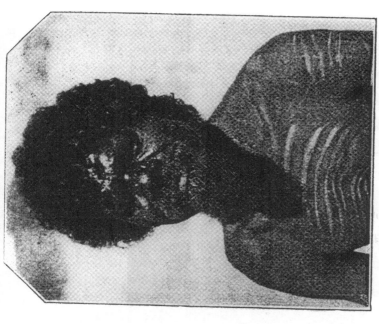

No. 28

Full Face of Nilotic Negro of First Exodus

Showing lygmy nose, "beetle-brows," cicatrisation marks, curly hair. No Hero-cult.

No. 29

NILOTIC NEGRO OF SECOND EXODUS

The markings here are tattoo and paintings, not cicatrisation. This is a higher type of development of the human. They have Hero-cult.

No. 30

TYPE OF SECOND EXODUS OF NILOTIC NEGRO

Tattoo marks, but little cicatrisation shown. A finer type and further developed human. They have Hero-cult.

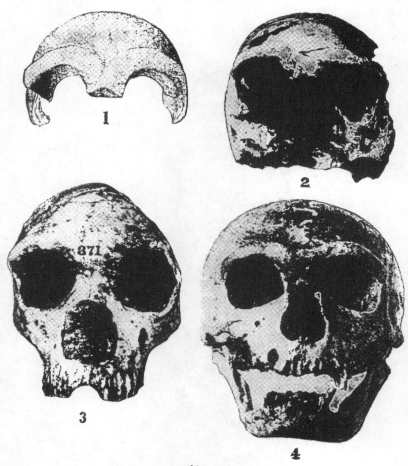

No. 31

1. The Neanderthal Skull with the heavy massive supra-orbital ridges.

2. The Spy Skull. These Skulls are those of Nilotic Negroes.

3. The Gibraltar. In the absence of any knowledge of the implements found
   with this I should put it as a highly developed Pygmy's, the cranial capacity
   being 1080 c.c. The average Pygmy's is 900 c.c. Those of the Tasmanians, however, who were highly developed Pygmies, average 1190 c.c., but
   many Nilotic Negroes have a cranial capacity of 1100 c.c.

4. From the burial position, and the implements found with this Skull, I should
   place it as that of an early Stellar Mythos Man or the latest exodus of Nilotic
   Negro.

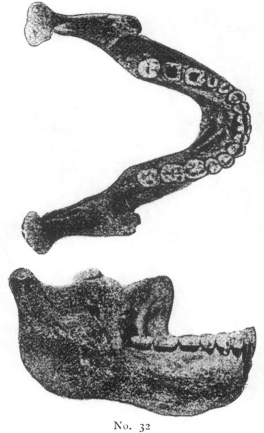

No. 32

The Lower Jaw of the Neanderthal Man, showing
the massive bony structure for the attachment of the
muscles for the setting of the teeth and mastication.

No. 33
Skeleton found at Harlyn Bay, Cornwall.
Stellar Mythos Man.

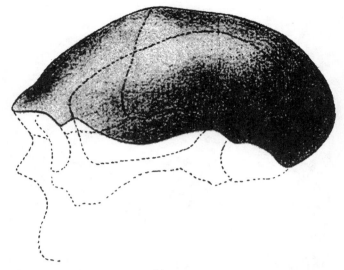

No. 34

The Cranium of the Pithecanthropus Erectus found in Java
during 1891 by Dr Du Bois. Cranial capacity, 850 c.c. I have
given a reconstruction of this Cranium here as that of Primary Man.

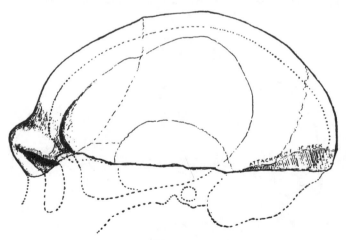

No. 35

The Neanderthal Cranium ($\frac{2}{3}$ natural size) orientated on the same
plane as the Modern English Man. It demonstrates the enormous
development of the supra-orbital ridges, showing the frontal lobe
and the greater development of the posterior part of Cranium—
in fact, that of a primary type of the Nilotic Negro. I have given
a reconstruction of the man.

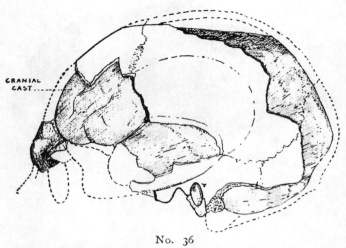

CRANIAL CAST

No. 36

The Ipswich Cranium profile drawing after Professor Keith. The Intercranial mass forms a cast of the brain on which the third frontal convolution is well marked. The frontal and occipital bones are fragmentary.

In this Cranium there is a greater supra-orbital ridge than in Modern Man, but much less than in the Neanderthal Man. The frontal lobe is not quite so well developed as in the Modern Man. I have given a reconstruction of this man.

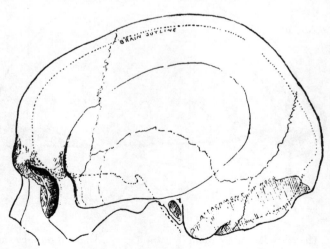

BRAIN OUTLINE

No. 37

Modern English Cranium ($\frac{2}{3}$ natural size) after Professor Keith. Showing the higher development of the frontal lobes of the brain and the lesser development of the posterior part.

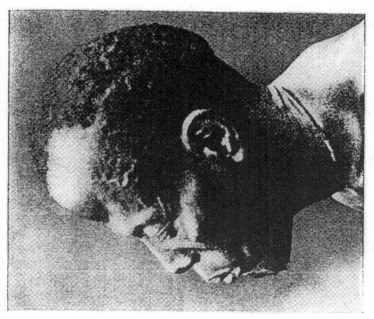

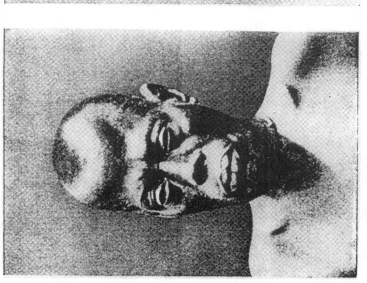

No. 38

Nilotic Negro, showing original types of big heads found in Europe.

By kind permission of Messrs Hutchinson & Co.:
the publishers of "The Uganda Protectorate." by Sir Harry Johnston, K.C.B., G.C.M.G.

Squatter.   Showing mode of sitting posture affecting the tibia in one way.

Squatter.

No. 39

No. 40
Squatters.
Showing modes of posture affecting the tibia in a different way.

No. 41

A Reconstruction of Primary Man.
Pithecanthropus Erectus.

No. 42

A Reconstruction of the Neanderthal Man.

No. 43

A Reconstruction of the Ipswich Man.

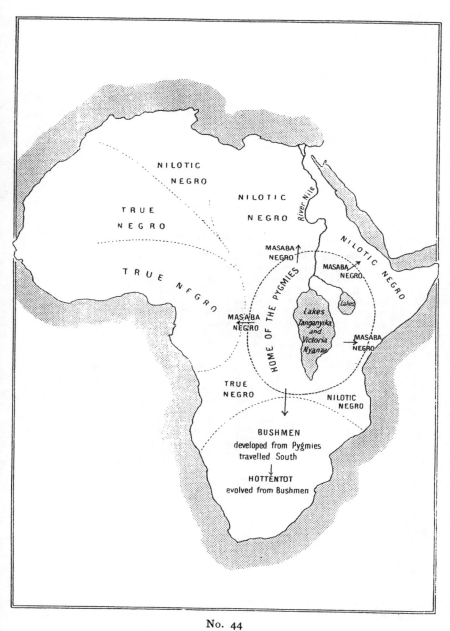

No. 44

MAP OF AFRICA
Showing the home of Primary Man.

MAP OF AFRICA

I here give a Map of Africa with the *two Great Lakes only*, as from all geological evidence there were then only *two Great Lakes*—the Victoria Nyanza and Tanganyika, now separated, were then only one. This is borne out by the ancient part of the ritual of the Old Egyptians, as also in the engraving on the scarab shown as an illustration. The dotted line around the Lakes shows the home of man ; those to the North, East and West, the spread of the Masaba Negro ; to the North and East, the spread of the Nilotic Negro ; and to the West, the true Negro. Those to the South show the Bushmen and their evolution into the Hottentots. The tables following these illustrations will give the reader more explicit information, besides being a further guide to the evolution of primary humans.

N. N. = Nilotic Negroes.
T. N. = True Negroes.
M. N. = Masaba Negroes.

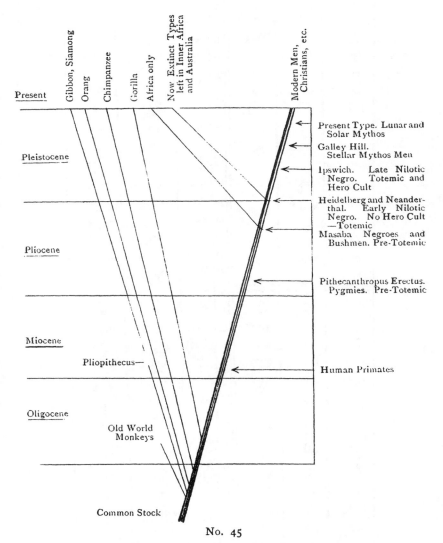

No. 45

A Genealogical Tree of Man and the Anthropoids.
Time from first Pygmy to present date = from one and a half to two million years.

No. 46

PURE EGYPTIAN HIEROGLYPHICS
Found in many parts of the world and tabulated as above
by the Author.

A tabulated and comparative list of pure Egyptian Hiero-glyphics discovered and thus depicted by me. As you will see, they are from North, Central and South America, Ireland, Scotland, Wales and England, and from Egypt. These will, I am sure, assist you in following the human race from their birthplace (Old Egypt) throughout the world.